Making Connections®

Reading Comprehension Skills and Strategies
Level Gold

EDUCATORS PUBLISHING SERVICE
Cambridge and Toronto

Contents

Be an Active Reader

We want you to write in this book! Marking the text helps you...

- remember what you've read
- understand what you've read
- answer questions about what you've read

As you read the texts in this book, you will

1. **mark for meaning** by circling words and phrases you can't read, or can read but don't understand. You will learn vocabulary strategies to help you figure these out.

2. **mark for skills** by underlining examples of the skills you are learning. The skills in this book are:

- main idea and details
- compare and contrast
- cause and effect
- making inferences
- figurative language
- recognizing persuasion

Below is an example of a marked text. This reader circled words and phrases she found difficult. Then she underlined similarities in blue and differences in green.

The Arctic and Antarctica are as far away from each other as you can get on Earth. Both regions are extremely cold. They have ice, snow, roaring winds, low clouds, and fog. However, the Arctic region is mostly water surrounded by land, while Antarctica is a continent surrounded by water. This difference is important to the people, plants, and animals that live there.

Against the Odds

🔥 A fire breaks out in the middle of the night. How will you escape?

🔥 A blanket of ash and stone sweeps down an angry mountain. Does anyone live to tell the tale?

🔥 A lone mountain climber suffers a terrible accident. What must he do to survive?

Unit 1

Main Idea and Details Main ideas are the most important ideas in a text. These ideas are supported by facts and examples called details.

FIRE!

What should you do if your house is on fire?

Where There's Smoke . . .

Your eyes flutter open. You yawn and start to roll over. Suddenly, your nose wrinkles. There's a strange smell, almost like something is—burning?! You jump out of bed and race down the hallway. You screech to a halt at the top of the stairs. Giant flames leap at the ceiling. A dark cloud of smoke fills the room. What will you do? How will you survive?

Firefighters work to extinguish a house fire.

. . . There's Fire

If you are ever in this situation, the most important thing is to get out of the house—and stay out. Don't stop to take anything with you. Don't even get dressed. Fires become very dangerous very quickly, and getting out fast is critical. The faster you act, the better your chances of escaping.

Getting out can be tricky. It's not a good idea to open doors and windows during a fire. A fire needs oxygen to burn. With more air, a fire grows more quickly, and the damage increases. In fact, close as many doors as possible in order to stop the fire from growing.

FAST FIRE

In just three minutes, the smallest fire can take over a whole room, if not the whole house.

If you do need to open a door to escape, test the doorknob by touching it with the back of your hand. If the doorknob is cool, open the door slowly. If it is hot, leave the door closed and find a different way to escape.

Smoke can be a problem when you're trying to escape. Smoke can be very dense, which makes it hard to see, and it is filled with chemicals that can make you drowsy. The chemicals are toxic, or deadly. To make it easier to breathe, cover your mouth and nose with a damp cloth. Stay low to the ground. Smoke rises, so crawling on the floor will make it easier to breathe.

HEATING UP

Temperatures in a house fire can reach more than 1,100°F. Even a room that is not on fire can reach a temperature of over 300°F!

A smoke detector

Stay low to the ground to avoid toxic smoke.

Preparation Is the Key

You can't always prevent a house fire, but you can be prepared for one. The most important thing is to make sure there are smoke detectors on every floor of your house. Change the batteries once or twice a year, just to ensure the detectors still work.

Your house should also be equipped with fire extinguishers and fire blankets. Fire extinguishers put out fires by cooling the fuel of the fire or removing oxygen that feeds the fire. They should be mounted near doorways. Fire blankets should be used to smother cooking fires. These blankets should be kept in an easy-to-reach place in the kitchen, away from the stove.

A fire extinguisher

And don't forget to plan—and practice—an escape route. Practicing an escape route is especially important for younger family members. Everyone should know how to get out of the house and where to meet once they're out. If possible, your plan should include alternate routes. A door or hallway may be blocked by fire.

A fire blanket

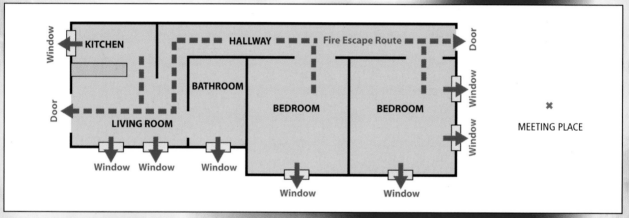

Plan a fire escape route.

Fires can be scary, but they can seem less scary if you are prepared. If you want to know more, contact your local fire department. And if you wake up one night to a house fire, you'll know just what to do—and how to survive.

FIRE: THE HUMAN COST

Each year, almost 4,000 Americans die in house fires. Another 2,000 are severely injured.

These are the leading causes of house fires:

- Cigarettes
- Electrical problems
- Arson
- Cooking

Practice the Skill

Main Idea and Details

1. Read the second paragraph on page 7. Write the main idea and three supporting details in the chart below.

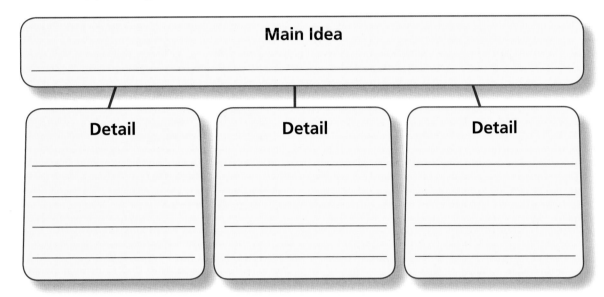

Main Idea
_____

Detail
_____
_____
_____
_____

Detail
_____
_____
_____
_____

Detail
_____
_____
_____
_____

2. Read the second paragraph on page 8. What is the main idea?

_____

_____

_____

How well do the paragraph details support the main idea? Explain.

_____

_____

Vocabulary

Define these words as they are used in the text.

- smother (page 8) _____

- alternate (page 8) _____

Escape from Pompeii

How did Antonius escape the fury of the volcano?

I had to run to keep up with Antonius, my master. I had never seen him so mad. As we moved through the crowded streets, the ground shook slightly. But tremors were nothing new to Pompeii.

Our task was important. Weeks ago, Antonius had ordered a supply of olive oil from the merchant Bassus. It still had not arrived. We had very little left. Like others in Pompeii, we used olive oil for food, fuel, and medicines.

I glanced up at Mount Vesuvius rising in the distance. The great mountain seemed friendly, as if it was watching over us.

Bassus was just coming out of his house when we arrived. Antonius sputtered a loud, long series of insults at him. I stood to the side and listened to the birds chirping in the trees.

Suddenly, over the shouting, there was a thunderous crack. We froze, and Antonius's hands stopped in midair. I turned toward Mount Vesuvius and gasped. The top of the mountain had split open and a cloud of smoke burst forth.

"How strange," Bassus said softly.

Bassus was merely curious, but Antonius was alarmed. While the smoke distracted Bassus, my master motioned for me to follow him. He stopped several feet away, where two of Bassus's horses were tied to a wooden post. He quietly untied one. Without a word, he lifted me on the horse's back and then climbed on in front of me.

Antonius glanced back at Bassus, who was still gazing in wonder at the mountain. Bassus was shocked when he saw us on his horse. "Where do you think you're going, thief? I told you, you'll get your oil tomorrow!"

"I'm borrowing your horse, Bassus," Antonius said, "as payment for your lateness. And I urge you to follow closely behind. That mountain is much angrier than I am."

Bassus stood dumbfounded, unable to respond. My master turned the horse, and we rode off.

Moments later, the first ash and stone fell on us. It was terrifying. The noise grew louder as a great fire burst from the mountain. Children were calling for their parents. Birds were zooming by us at full speed. Even the horse we were riding seemed anxious.

Antonius was pushing the horse as hard as he could.

"Master?" I asked over the noise. "Where are we going?"

His response was abrupt. "Away from Pompeii."

I was shocked. "What! Leave Pompeii?"

"Do you remember the earthquake, Marcus?" His voice grew quieter. "It was more than fifteen years ago. Perhaps you were too young."

"I've heard about it," I said loudly. He had forgotten that my entire family had perished in the earthquake, leaving me alone in the world.

"Most of the town was damaged, and I lost everything," Antonius continued. He pointed toward Mount Vesuvius. "I'm not waiting to see what the gods have planned for me this time."

As we made our way out of town, it was clear that Pompeii was in a state of confusion. People were running around frantically. An older woman raised her arms and cried out to the mountain, "What have we done?" We saw people boarding up their windows and closing their doors. We heard a father call to his crying children, "Go inside. You'll be safe there."

Some people were trying to save their possessions. One man staggered under the weight of a heavy chair. His cart already held several beautiful works of art. Two women were wearing their best clothing and jewelry. A few others, like us, were on horseback and carried nothing.

Just outside Pompeii, it was chaos. The ash and stone, mixed with some kind of fiery material, fell heavily. People around us were going in all different directions. Some were headed toward the sea. Others were headed south. No one rode toward Rome—angry Mount Vesuvius stood in the way.

Antonius and I moved quickly with no possessions to slow us down. The ash continued to pile up. Day turned into night as Mount Vesuvius's black cloud filled the sky and swallowed the sun.

The horse was moving slowly now. It was exhausted, and so was I. It felt like we had been riding for days, although it was only the middle of the night. We stopped on a hill to let the panting horse catch its breath.

We raised our eyes from the road and glanced back at Mount Vesuvius. At that moment an avalanche of fiery ash and rock gushed down the side of the mountain. It swept forward, like a scroll unrolling, covering everything in its path. I thought of Bassus and all the others we had passed along the way. I hoped they had all survived.

Eventually, we found an inn. We rested and ate. We worried about our friends. Several days passed. The skies cleared, but still we heard no news from Pompeii.

I was ready when my master said we would go back. As we approached the city, we understood why there had been no news. Pompeii had completely disappeared. In its place lay a solid, smooth blanket of ash and stone. The blanket covered everything—trees, houses, and the larger buildings. And it must have been at least ten feet deep. Nothing looked familiar. Antonius looked on silently.

"What now?" I whispered.

My master turned the horse around again. We rode back to the inn, where we started our lives over again. Once in a while, we would meet another survivor from Pompeii. More often, we tried to forget the horrors of that day and the destruction we had seen.

Practice the Skill

Main Idea and Details

1. Look at the fourth paragraph on page 11, beginning "Moments later." In the chart below, write the main idea in your own words. Then write three details that support it.

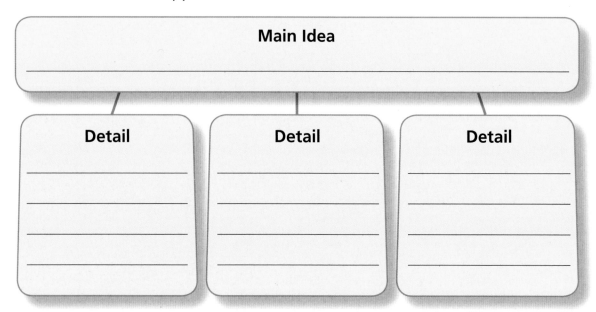

Main Idea

_____

Detail	Detail	Detail
_____	_____	_____

2. What is the main idea of page 12? Write it in your own words.

_____

_____

Write three details that support this main idea.

- _____
- _____
- _____

Check Comprehension

What events signaled that Mount Vesuvius was about to erupt?

_____

_____

Bad Day for Pompeii

Read the fourth paragraph on page 13, beginning "I was ready."
Write the main idea of this paragraph in the box below.

Vocabulary

1. Find the word *insults* on page 10. Write a sentence using this word.

   _____

   _____

2. Write the phrase from page 11 that tells what *dumbfounded* means.

   _____

3. What does the word *anxious* on page 11 mean?

   _____

Writing

How would Antonius explain why he and Marcus were able to escape the volcano?

THE COST OF SURVIVAL

How did Aron Ralston's amazing courage help him get to safety?

The Start of an Adventure

Aron Ralston had planned an easy hiking trip for April 26, 2003. The twenty-seven-year-old was an experienced mountain climber. He had climbed most of Colorado's "fourteeners," or mountains that are at least 14,000 feet high. He had climbed many of them alone. That April day, Ralston went to Blue John Canyon, a remote spot in Utah.

Ralston packed only for the day. He had three liters of water, four candy bars, and two burritos. He also brought his climbing equipment, camera, and CD player. He parked his car and rode his bike fifteen miles to the canyon. He had another fifteen miles to travel on foot.

Caught in the Canyon

The first several miles were uneventful. Then Ralston came to a group of boulders that were wedged between the canyon walls. He had climbed over several of them when one of the boulders began to move. Ralston could not get out of the way fast enough. Before he knew it, his right arm and hand were pinned between an 800-pound boulder and the canyon wall.

For forty-five minutes, Ralston thrashed against the boulder, trying to free his arm. Nothing worked. Exhausted and sweating, he grabbed his water bottle and took a long drink. He had just downed one-third of his water supply.

The space where Ralston was stuck for five days

The Choice

Ralston forced himself to calm down. He had three options. He could use his pocket knife to chip away enough of the boulder to free his arm. Another choice was to put together a pulley with his climbing equipment. He could use the pulley to lift the boulder and pull out his arm. The last option was to amputate, or cut off, his own arm.

Aron Ralston took this photo as he was trapped by the boulder.

As the hours ticked by, Ralston went through each of his options. His pocket knife could not do more than scrape the boulder. Chipping at it would not work. His pulley system barely moved the boulder. And when it came to cutting off his arm, Ralston's pocket knife alone would not be enough. The knife might cut skin and muscle, but it was not strong enough to cut through the bone.

Even if Ralston did free himself by amputating his arm, he would still face a huge challenge. He would have to lower himself to the canyon floor sixty-five feet below, hike seven miles through the desert, climb 800 feet out of the canyon, and drive two hours on dirt roads to get medical help. His prospects did not look good.

Life and Death

The next few days passed slowly. Ralston did not have much food. Then he ran out of water. The nights were freezing cold. Ralston did not want to free himself at night. He did not want to walk around the canyon in the dark.

Five days had gone by. Ralston was so convinced he was going to die that night, he scratched his own epitaph into the canyon wall. He wrote his name (Aron), the dates of his birth and likely death (Oct 75–Apr 03), and "RIP" for "rest in peace."

Taking Action

But Ralston did not die on April 30. The next day, he noticed his right hand was decomposing. He panicked. He thrashed around violently, trying desperately to free himself. As Ralston threw himself back and forth, he realized something: if he broke the bones in his arm, he could amputate the arm.

Ralston immediately set to work. The pain was unbelievable, but he struggled on at his grim task. An hour later, he was free. Joy and shock washed over him. He would make it out of the canyon.

There was no time to waste. Ralston created a makeshift sling to control the bleeding and protect his arm. He sorted through all of his possessions, leaving behind as much as possible. He grabbed his climbing rope and stumbled through the canyon. There was no room for mistakes. Ralston approached the Big Drop, a cliff about six stories high. He would have to lower himself down the cliff with ropes—and only one hand.

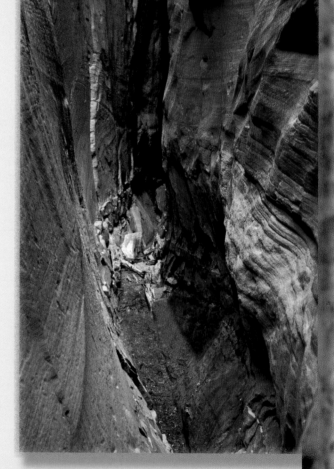

Ralston managed to lower himself down the Big Drop.

Peering over the cliff, Ralston saw a muddy pool of water at the bottom. Water. The thought made him dizzy. He forced himself to focus. Ralston used his mouth and left hand to carefully set up the rope, ease over the ledge, and slide down. Once he reached the bottom, Ralston gulped the dirty water, which tasted sweet in his parched mouth. He filled his water containers again and again.

The Final Frontier

Ralston refilled his water containers one more time before heading into the sun-drenched canyon. He had an seven-mile hike ahead of him. Soon, most of his water was gone. To keep from dehydrating, Ralston held water in his mouth without swallowing it. That technique helped him ration his water supply.

After six difficult miles, Ralston was bleeding heavily. But suddenly he saw people. "Help!" he called. "I need help!" The family who heard his cries knew a hiker was missing. As Ralston came toward them, he blurted out his story. Two of them ran ahead for help, and the third walked with Ralston for another mile.

As they approached the exit trail, Ralston heard a loud rumbling. A helicopter landed on the canyon floor. A man got out and shouted, "Are you Aron?" Ralston had made it. He was forty pounds lighter and short one arm, but he had survived.

"I had made all of the choices . . . that had helped me survive. I took responsibility for all of my decisions, which helped me take on the responsibility of getting myself out."
Aron Ralston

Practice the Skill

Main Idea and Details

Read the main idea of the section The Start of an Adventure below. Then write three details from the text that support it.

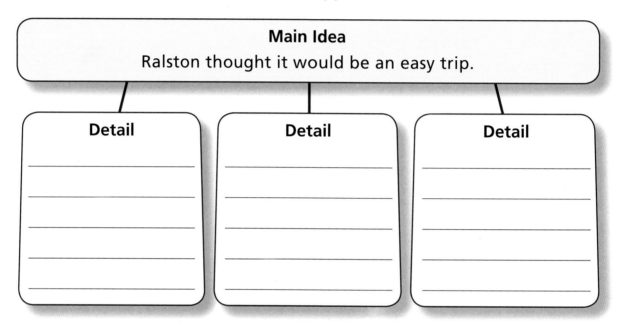

Main Idea
Ralston thought it would be an easy trip.

Detail	Detail	Detail

Check Comprehension

Look at the section The Choice. Write Ralston's three options and why they did not work.

Options	Why Options Did Not Work
1. _____	1. _____
2. _____	2. _____
3. _____	3. _____

A Matter of Life and Death

1. Look at the section Taking Action on pages 18–19. Why is that a good name for this section?

   _____

   _____

   _____

   _____

   _____

2. Write the main idea of the whole text.

   _____

   _____

   _____

   _____

Vocabulary

1. What is the meaning of *remote* on page 16?

   _____

2. Find the word *makeshift* on page 18. Write a sentence using this word.

   _____

   _____

3. What is the meaning of *parched* on page 19?

   _____

Writing

In preparing for his trip, what might Ralston have done differently in order to be rescued sooner?

Text Connections

Now that you have read some texts about survival, choose one of the following topics to investigate.

- 🔥 As a class, use the main ideas from the text "Fire!" to help you write a Fire Escape Manual for your school. Then find out if your school already has one. Compare them and see if there is anything missing from either manual.

- 🔥 Pompeii was buried by the eruption of Mt. Vesuvius in 79 CE. What was life like at that time? What were people doing? Use books and the Internet to find out more about Pompeii. Display your findings on a poster and share with the class.

- 🔥 Research another volcano, such as Mt. St. Helens in Washington state or Mt. Etna in Italy. Write an account of its last eruption. Tell how it happened, when it happened, and what the result was. Include pictures if possible.

- 🔥 Write a fiction or nonfiction survival story. Remember to include vivid supporting details in your writing.

- 🔥 Create a poster that provides safety guidelines for hiking or another outdoor sport. Include labeled pictures of supplies and safety gear.

Continue your explorations by reading these books:

Castaway Survivor's Guide by Rory Storm
Could you survive in the wild with only your hands and your head to help you? Learn how with this book!

Death Mountain by Sherry Shahan
Erin and Mae are lost in the Sierra Nevada mountains. Will they find their way back to civilization?

Hatchet by Gary Paulson
Brian survived the plane crash. Can he survive alone in the wilderness?

Going to Extremes:
The Arctic and Antarctica

❋ **A blizzard rages. Ice cracks underfoot. It's way below zero. What creatures live in these extremes?**

❋ **Two teens move to new towns and new schools. Can their e-mail friendship help them cope?**

❋ **Two explorers race for the South Pole. Which man will win? Which man will not return?**

Unit 2

Compare and Contrast To compare and contrast, identify how things, people, places, or ideas are similar and how they are different.

Poles Apart

How are the polar regions alike? How are they different?

The Arctic and Antarctica are as far away from each other as you can get on Earth. Both polar regions are extremely cold. They have ice, snow, roaring winds, low clouds, and fog. They both have summer days when the sun never sets, and winter nights that can last from twenty-four hours to six months! However, the Arctic region is mostly water surrounded by land, while Antarctica is a continent surrounded by water. This difference is important to the people, plants, and animals that live there.

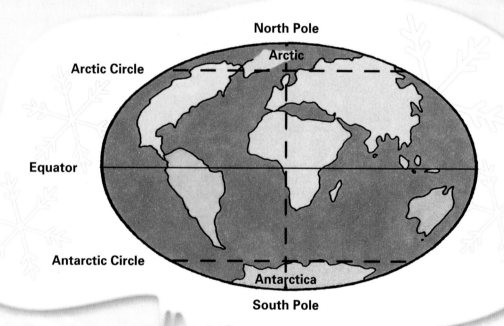

What Lives in the Extreme Cold?

The land in the Arctic is a treeless plain called tundra. Much of the ground is always frozen. Trees can't live there because of the strong, cold winds, but mosses, grasses, and low bushes can survive. In the summer, much of the Arctic snow and ice melts, and wildflowers bloom.

A modern Inuit village

Animals such as caribou, seals, and arctic fox have adapted to the extreme cold. Native peoples such as the Inuit have also learned to live in the harsh conditions. They caught fish, and hunted sea and land mammals. In the past, they used animal skins to make tents and clothing. In the summer, most Inuit lived in tents. In the winter, they moved into sod houses. Igloos, or shelters made of snow, were used on hunting trips.

In contrast, almost nothing can live in the icy center of Antarctica. A few tiny plants and animals survive on the ice. Seals, penguins, and fish live on the edges of the continent and in the waters around it. Their bodies have also adapted to the cold. The only people found in Antarctica are scientists who visit research stations such as McMurdo Station.

Freezing Facts

	Arctic Region	Antarctica
Average temperature	0° at the North Pole	−60° at the South Pole
Average thickness of ice	10 to 20 feet	7,000 feet
Number of people permanently living there	15 million	0
Continent?	no	yes

 Polar bears and penguins are probably the most famous residents of the polar regions. But the only place they will ever meet is in the zoo! Now find out how and where they live . . .

Huge Bears and Tiny Penguins

Although they live at opposite ends of Earth, polar bears and penguins have one important thing in common: they are both well adapted to living in the cold.

Polar bear   Adult human   Adélie penguin

Polar bears, the largest members of the bear family, are found in the Arctic. They can weigh up to 1,760 pounds. Compared to polar bears, Adélie (uh-DAY-lee) penguins are tiny! The smallest penguins in Antarctica, Adélies weigh only about eleven pounds.

Polar bear

Fur and Feathers Polar bears aren't bothered by the cold. Each strand of their white fur is hollow and traps body heat. Below this white fur, a polar bear's skin is actually black. A four-inch layer of fat lies just under the polar bear's skin. This layer of blubber helps keep the bear warm.

Adélie penguins don't need fur to stay warm. Their thick layers of oily feathers repel water and trap air to save body heat. Like polar bears, Adélie penguins also have a layer of fat under the skin.

Alone or Together? Polar bears usually live alone. Seals are their main food source. Polar bears hunt seals by waiting for them—very quietly—beside a breathing hole in the ice. When a seal surfaces to breathe, the bear grabs the seal with its teeth and lifts it onto the ice.

Adélie penguins

Unlike polar bears, Adélie penguins live in large groups on the rocky coasts or islands of Antarctica. Adélie adults can be gone for three days at a time hunting food for their chicks. They mostly eat krill, which are small shrimp-like animals.

These huge bears and tiny penguins are poles apart, but they are both cold-weather experts.

Practice the Skill

Compare and Contrast Two Regions

Write two similarities and two differences between the Arctic and Antarctica.

How are they similar?

- _____
- _____

How are they different?

- _____
- _____

Similarities

List three similarities between polar bears and Adélie penguins.

- _____
- _____
- _____

Polar bears

Adélie penguins

Differences

List three differences between polar bears and Adélie penguins.

- _____
- _____
- _____

Vocabulary

1. Why are Antarctica and the Arctic called "polar regions"?

    _____

2. Use the word *tundra* in a sentence that shows its meaning.

    _____

    _____

ALASKA E-MAIL PIPELINE

To: Jessica@farnorth.net ▲ Send ▲ Reply ▲ Forward ▲ Delete

From: Aniksuaq@ealaska.net

Sent: March 10

Subject: Hello!

Dear Jessica,

Hi! Welcome to Alaska! I'm glad you joined the Middle School Alaska E-mail Pipeline. My name is Aniksuaq, but everyone calls me Nik. I guess that makes it my "nikname." :-)
My family is Inupiat, and I was named for my great-grandmother. She still lives in St. Nicholas, the village where I grew up. My dad, two brothers, and I moved south to Juneau last July, so I've done the new town, new school thing too.

Moving was a big change for me. Juneau is HUGE compared to where I used to live. My middle school here is gigantic compared to my last school—750 kids instead of 150! I pretty much knew everyone back home, and they all knew me and my family. That was good and bad—I had lots of friends I'd known forever, but sometimes I didn't have any privacy, if you know what I mean. It took a while, but I've made a bunch of new friends here.

Sorry, I've just been rambling on about myself. Please tell me all about you. Where are you from? What is your family like? What do you do for fun? How do you like Alaska so far?

Write back soon,
Nik

To: Aniksuaq@ealaska.net ▲ Send ▲ Reply ▲ Forward ▲ Delete
From: Jessica@farnorth.net
Sent: March 14
Subject: RE: Hello!

Hi Nik,

Thanks for writing! You weren't rambling—it was great to learn about you. I'm glad to have someone to talk to. It seems like all the kids here already have their own cliques.

I just moved to Alaska two months ago. I'm stuck in Fox, which is way up north, even for Alaska (you probably know that). I used to live in Texas. My dad works for an oil company and was transferred up here to work on the "real" Alaska pipeline (not the e-mail version). For work, he goes even farther north, way inside the Arctic Circle.

My mom says I should stop complaining, but I HATE it here. Fox is SOOOO small compared to Houston. There's nothing to do! You're so lucky you moved to a city. My school is really small too. Back home I was in the drama club and the filmmakers' club, but they don't have anything like that here. My dad bought me a video camera to make up for dragging me here but there's nothing I want to film.

Plus…it's freezing, even in March! Will winter ever end? In Houston, summer lasted forever. I can't believe how everyone here is into outdoor sports, even in the snow. I hate sports, and I hate the cold! I wish I could have stayed in Texas with my grandmother. She lives right on the beach. Sunbathing is MY kind of sport. :-) And you know what the worst thing is? My little brother loves Alaska. He went right from waterskiing to cross country!

Please write back soon—before I freeze to death!

Your friend (I hope),
Jess

To: Jessica@farnorth.net
From: Aniksuaq@ealaska.net
Sent: March 19
Subject: Family and Friends

▲ Send ▲ Reply ▲ Forward ▲ Delete

Dear Jess,

Oh no! I'm sorry you're having such a tough time. Moving IS hard. I know you love the city, but I didn't like it at first. There are so many people you don't know. It was a little scary. And I missed my old friends.

Funny you said you wanted to stay with your grandmother. One of the hardest things for me was leaving my great-grandma. She wouldn't leave St. Nicholas. My *aaka* is really into the old ways of our people. I used to love listening to her stories. But now she's giving me a hard time. She says I'm forgetting my "roots"—the Inupiat stories and the language. She quizzes me all the time about what I'm doing in "the big bad city" and what I remember of the old ways. I really missed her at first, but now it's kind of annoying to talk to her.

It took a while, but I finally like Juneau. You're right, there is a lot to do here—stores and movie theaters and kids from all over. I probably shouldn't tell you this, but it's a lot warmer in Juneau than it is in Fox. Winters don't get much below freezing, and it's T-shirt weather in the summertime. We're even getting ready for our Spring Festival. We could use you down here! We're supposed to film the festival for the Technology Club but I'm not that into it. The most I can handle is a lame tape recorder. :-) I'm pathetic at techie stuff, but I joined the club because there's this cute boy in it…

Here's an idea. Maybe you could use your video camera to record your Spring Festival (does your school have one?). Then you could edit it into your own movie. I bet lots of kids would like to star in it. What do you think?

Good luck!
Nik

To: Aniksuaq@ealaska.net   ▲ Send   ▲ Reply   ▲ Forward   ▲ Delete

From: Jessica@farnorth.net

Sent: March 21

Subject: Good ideas!

Hey Nik,

Thanks for your great idea! I got up the nerve to talk to a couple of kids in my class (I never really did that before), and they love the idea of starring in a movie. It's the strangest thing…before I brought up the movie, they actually thought *I* was unfriendly. Can you believe it???!!

Now I have an idea for you. Don't worry, it's not very techie. :-) Instead of filming the festival, you could use your (lame) tape recorder to do an oral history of your great-grandma and her Inupiat stories when you visit St. Nicholas next. Maybe some of her friends have stories too. Just let them speak into the tape recorder. Maybe that cute boy can help you transfer the files to your computer and make CDs of them. That way your *aaka* will know you want to keep a connection to the old ways. And who knows about the boy…

Let me know how it turns out. OK, I've got to go. I've got a lot to do to prepare for the movie. I'll keep you posted and send you a copy of the movie when it's done.

Talk to you soon.

Friends forever,
Jess

Race to the Bottom of the World!

What differences led to the outcome of this race?

In 1911, an amazing race took place across the Antarctic continent!

Two groups of men fought their way through the harshest climate in the world. Each group was determined to be the first ever to reach the South Pole. They wanted to bring glory to their nations—and to themselves. The two groups were led by men who were similar in some ways but very different in other ways. Because of these differences—and some bad luck—only one of these leaders would survive the race to the bottom of the world.

Robert Scott

Robert Scott was in a hurry. He was already a famous explorer in 1910, and he had been to Antarctica before. When Scott, an Englishman, heard that German and French expeditions to the South Pole were being planned, he wanted to beat them.

Scott hastily selected some sled dogs. However, he thought dogs were not reliable so he decided to use ponies to pull his sleds. He ignored advice that ponies were not suitable for Antarctic conditions. Scott also took new motorized sleds, even though they had not been carefully tested in extreme conditions.

Scott was known as a brave leader who always made important decisions on his own. For this expedition, he chose a large party of sixty-five men. Because Scott was in such a hurry, Scott's men did not have time to learn to ski well.

One of the ponies Scott used to pull his sleds

Roald Amundsen

Compared with Scott, the Norwegian explorer Roald Amundsen planned his expedition very carefully. He had never been to Antarctica, but he had explored the Arctic. He had learned a lot from the native people there. Amundsen could build igloos for shelter and knew which skins and furs provided the warmest clothing. He also knew how to make sleds run smoothly over the snow. Amundsen read all he could about Antarctica and talked to experts. He chose the best sled dogs and trained them well. Like many Norwegians, Amundsen was an expert skier, and he made sure that all of the nineteen men on his expedition were too.

Roald Amundsen

The Race Is On!

Scott's expedition left England on the ship *Terra Nova* on June 1, 1910. During the journey south, Scott received a telegram from Amundsen, announcing that his ship, the *Fram,* had already started for Antarctica. Both men knew the race was on!

Both expeditions reached Antarctica safely. Scott landed at McMurdo Sound and Amundsen at the Bay of Whales. They planned different routes to the South Pole. Both teams set up base camps and made trips inland to bury supplies for their return trips from the pole.

Amundsen and his ship, the *Fram*

Victory and Defeat

On October 19, 1911, Amundsen and four companions skimmed off across the snow with four sleds pulled by dogs. They had high-calorie supplies for four months—enough for their race to the South Pole.

Scott in his hut in Antarctica

At the last minute, Scott added a fifth man to the team that was traveling overland to the pole. They left for the pole on November 1, 1911. Almost at once, the motors of their motorized sleds froze. The ponies began to die. The men had to drag the sleds themselves.

On December 14, 1911, Amundsen and his men reached the South Pole. They had traveled over crumpled ice ridges and through thick fog. Two men had been rescued after falling into crevasses—deep open cracks in the ice. But they had all made it! Amundsen wrote in his diary:

> At three in the afternoon a simultaneous "Halt!" rang out from the drivers. They had carefully examined their sledge-meters and they all showed a full distance — our Pole by reckoning. The goal was reached, the journey ended.

Amundsen returned victorious to his base camp, picking up buried supplies along the way.

Meanwhile, Scott's expedition was in trouble. They were traveling slowly. The extra team member meant that food was short. Still, they refused to turn back. Finally, on January 18, 1912, they reached the South Pole—and were bitterly disappointed. They found Amundsen's flag, a tent, and a note with the names of Amundsen's team and the date: December 14, 1911. Scott and his team had lost the race.

Amundsen and his dog team at the South Pole

Tragedy Strikes

Scott's team now turned back toward base camp, but much of the fuel at their supply depots had vaporized. Heating, cooking, and even melting snow for water was difficult. Then a raging blizzard set in. Two of Scott's men died of exhaustion. The remaining three, including Scott himself, had to pull sleds loaded with scientific samples Scott had insisted on collecting. They set up camp to wait out the blizzard.

Scott's men pulling their sled

Scott wrote in his diary:

Every day we have been ready to start for our depot 11 miles away, but outside the door of the tent it remains a scene of whirling drift. I do not think we can hope for any better things now. We shall stick it out to the end, but we are getting weaker, of course, and the end cannot be far. It seems a pity, but I do not think I can write more.

R. Scott

All three men died.

The Legend

When the news reached London, a newspaper wrote that "Scott and his fellow heroes" had brought honor to England by the way they behaved "in the closing hours of their lives."

Scott and his team. They all died in Antarctica.

Amundsen had won the race, but Scott became the legend. His tragic diary described brave men overwhelmed by the forces of nature. It told how they had faced death with courage. In the end, it was Scott who became famous for the expedition to the South Pole. He became known as "Scott of the Antarctic."

Practice the Skill

Compare and Contrast

Look on pages 34–35 to fill in the Venn diagram. Write three similarities and two differences in the ways that Scott and Amundsen prepared for the race to the South Pole.

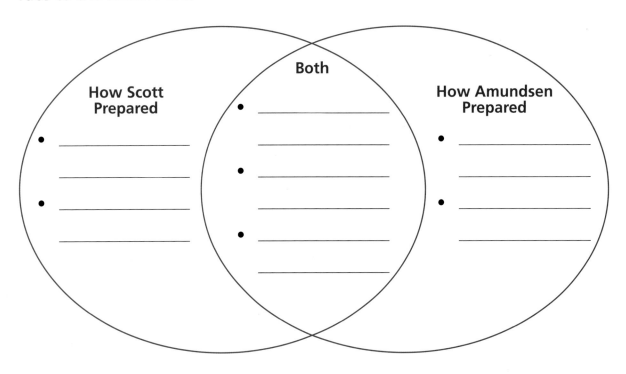

How Scott Prepared

Both

How Amundsen Prepared

Check Comprehension

1. Why did Scott and Amundsen want to reach the South Pole?

_____

_____

2. Why did Scott decide to use ponies to pull his sleds?

_____

_____

3. What three things did Amundsen learn from the people of the Arctic?

- _____

- _____

- _____

Who Did It?

Look on pages 36–37 to answer these questions. Write either Scott or Amundsen.

1. Who used only dogs to pull his sleds?	
2. Who added an extra person to his team at the last minute?	
3. Which man was able to reach his buried supplies on the way back?	
4. Which man refused to turn back when his expedition was in trouble?	
5. Who faced a terrible blizzard?	

Vocabulary

1. Write the sentence from page 36 that tells what *crevasses* means.

_____

_____

2. Use the word *expedition* in a sentence that shows its meaning.

_____

_____

Writing

What do you think is the most important reason Amundsen won the race to the South Pole? Explain why you think so.

Text Connections

Now that you have read several texts about the Arctic and Antarctica, do some exploring on your own. Choose from the topics below.

※ Did you know that the polar regions are in danger from human activity? Research the effects of global warming on these two environments. Then write a magazine article describing what you've learned.

※ Write a poem about the Arctic or Antarctica. You may want to start with a line from one of the texts.

※ Find out about the race to be the first to reach the North Pole. Write a report telling who won and why.

※ Go to the Web site of the United States Antarctic Program (**http://www.usap.gov**) and find the link to the *Antarctic Sun* newspaper. Compare and contrast the stories from this paper to the news in your hometown newspaper. Then present your findings to your class.

※ Continue the e-mail correspondence between Nik and Jess. You may want to write about what happened with their new projects.

※ Do research on how to build an igloo. Write step-by-step instructions and include drawings or diagrams.

Continue your explorations by reading these books:

Julie of the Wolves by Jean Craighead George
See how an Inuit girl survives on the Arctic tundra—with help from a pack of wolves.

Matthew Henson and the North Pole Expedition by Ann Graham Gaines
Follow this African American explorer on a 1909 expedition. Were these explorers the first to reach the North Pole?

City Bear by Dougal Dixon
Watch a wild polar bear cub grow up—a bit too close to human beings.

CRIME AND PUNISHMENT

- A hall monitor hands out unfair punishments—until someone stands up to him.

- Three famous outlaws were hunted because of their crimes. Were they caught?

- The ancient Greek god Prometheus tricks Zeus, his king. How does Zeus teach him a lesson?

Unit
3

Cause and Effect   A cause is why something happens, and an effect is the result.

School Rules

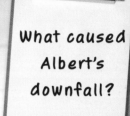

What caused Albert's downfall?

Max was walking down the hall minding his own business when Albert stopped him. Albert was the hall monitor. He took his job very seriously. "Halt!" ordered Albert. "Where do you think you're going?"

Max shrugged. "Class," he said. "And if you keep talking to me, I'm going to be late."

Albert pointed at Max's shirt. "Look, your shirt is untucked—which is forbidden in these halls—so I'm writing you up. As punishment, I order you to clean Mr. Crenshaw's classroom after school!"

"That's insane!" said Max. "There's no rule about tucking in your shirt. You made it up!"

"You don't believe me? Go ask the principal."

"Fine. I will," Max said. He had had just about enough of Albert and his ridiculous rules.

Max went to see the principal at lunchtime. "Ms. Martinez," he said. "I think Albert has gone too far. He's punishing me because my shirt was untucked. Isn't that crazy?"

Ms. Martinez looked up from her desk. "Look, Max, I'm really busy," she said. "Albert's the best hall monitor we've got. I'm sure you got what you deserved. Now if you don't mind, I'd like to get back to work."

Frustrated, Max left the principal's office. She hadn't even listened to him. Max had no choice but to do what Albert wanted.

When Max showed up at Mr. Crenshaw's classroom after school, Albert was waiting for him. "Clean the desks first, then the floors. I want this room spotless!" said Albert. He shoved an armful of cleaning supplies at Max.

Max gave Albert a dirty look. "I know you made up that rule, Albert, and I'm going to prove it."

"Oh, please!" snorted Albert. "It's in the official hall monitor rules. Now, I'm going to check on some other students. I'll be back soon, so no funny stuff!"

Max reflected on what Albert had said. "Hall monitor rules, huh?" he thought. "I bet Albert's stupid rule isn't there." That gave Max an idea. He checked the hallway and headed back to the principal's office.

"Can I help you, dear?" said Ms. Jenson, Ms. Martinez's assistant.

"Is Ms. Martinez still here?" asked Max. "I'd like to see the hall monitor rules."

"She's on the phone right now. But I have a copy right here." Ms. Jenson reached into a file drawer and handed Max a sheet of paper.

"Thanks, Ms. Jenson!" said Max. He scanned the rules. "No running, no horseplay—there's nothing in here about tucking in shirts!"

Just then, the principal emerged from her office. "Ms. Martinez! Albert's been making up rules, and I have proof!" Max handed her the rules. "Look! There's no rule about tucking in shirts!"

"Wait," said Ms. Martinez. "Albert wrote you up because your shirt was untucked? That's outrageous!"

Max sighed. "That's what I thought!"

"I'll put a stop to this," said Ms. Martinez. "Let's find Albert."

Max brought Ms. Martinez to Mr. Crenshaw's classroom. Albert sat at the teacher's desk with a scowl on his face. "Where have you been?" he said. "I'll have you cleaning every classroom in the school for this! Thanks for finding him, Ms. Martinez."

"Game's over, Albert," she replied sternly. "I know you've been making up rules. Why would you do such a thing? And what's this about having students clean classrooms? You can't do that!"

Albert's eyes widened in fear as he came up with an excuse. "Well . . . um . . . they deserved it!"

"No, we didn't," said Jim, appearing in the doorway. "You just punish people you don't like."

Just then, three more students entered the classroom.

"Albert's a liar. I got punished for having short hair!" said Lee.

"And I got punished for carrying too many books!" said Erica.

"He didn't even give me a reason!" said Sean. "He just said, 'You know what you did!' and made me stay after school."

Ms. Martinez was furious. "Albert, because of your actions, I am stripping you of your hall monitor duties. And I'm giving you three months' detention! Now hand over your hall monitor sash."

Max and the other students smiled smugly as Albert gave her the sash. Ms. Martinez turned to Max. "I'm sorry I didn't listen to you earlier."

"That's okay," said Max. "Thanks for helping me stop Albert."

"No, Max, thank you!" Ms. Martinez thought for a moment. "Max, a hall monitor position just opened up. How would you like to take it?"

Max smiled. "I would love to," he said. "I promise to enforce the rules—the real ones!"

Practice the Skill

Cause and Effect

1. Look at the first section of page 42. Write two effects of Max's shirt being untucked.

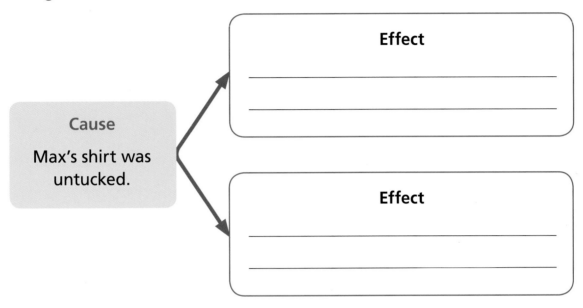

Cause

Max's shirt was untucked.

Effect

_____

_____

Effect

_____

_____

2. Look at the second section of page 42. Why did Max have to do what Albert wanted?

_____

_____

Check Comprehension

How did Max prove that Albert was making up rules?

_____

Vocabulary

1. Write a word from page 43 that means "read quickly."

_____

2. What does *emerged* mean on page 43?

_____

LEGENDARY OUTLAWS

Why did these outlaws choose a life of crime?

WANTED

Robin Hood

CRIME: Stealing from the rich to give to the poor

The Heroic Outlaw

The legend of Robin Hood comes from England, and it is more than 600 years old. Most experts believe that Robin Hood was not a real person. They say the legend was passed on because people like to hear about heroes who fight for the rights of others.

In one version of his story, Robin Hood was a wealthy landowner who left his home to fight in a war. When Robin returned, he discovered that the cruel Sheriff of Nottingham had taken his land and money.

The sheriff tried to capture Robin, but he escaped to Sherwood Forest. There, he met others who had been forced out of their homes by the sheriff. Many of these men agreed to help Robin fight the sheriff. They became known as Robin Hood's "Merry Men."

The Merry Men told Robin how the sheriff forced the poor to pay more and more taxes. As a result, the people could hardly feed their families. Instead of using the taxes to do good, the greedy sheriff kept the money for himself and his rich friends.

Robin was outraged. He and his men began stealing rich people's money and giving it away to poor people in nearby villages. Soon more and more people joined Robin in his cause. In time, he and his Merry Men overthrew the wicked sheriff and restored order to Nottingham.

Though Robin Hood may never have lived, his legend lives on. His compassion for the poor makes him both an outlaw and a hero in the minds of those who hear his tale.

The Outback Outlaw

Ned Kelly and the Kelly Gang lived in Australia at the end of the 1800s. Some people say Ned Kelly and his gang were cruel criminals. Others say they only fought for their rights against unfair laws and leaders.

During his teenage years, Ned Kelly was jailed four times for stealing. He thought the police treated him unfairly. As a result, Ned did not respect the police.

When Ned was nineteen, he tried to reform and be a good citizen. He got an honest job cutting down trees on a farm. But things did not go as planned. When several animals were stolen from the farm, the police blamed Ned. He felt that the police were unfairly harassing him for a crime he didn't commit.

Ned became frustrated. It did not seem to matter that he was trying to be good. People still thought he was a thief, so he figured he might as well be one. He took up stealing horses, and later formed the Kelly Gang with his brother Dan and two friends.

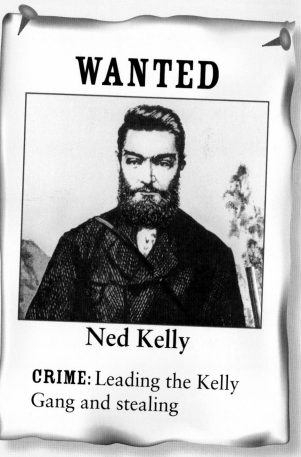

WANTED

Ned Kelly

CRIME: Leading the Kelly Gang and stealing

Fighting Authority

It was not long before the police came after the Kelly Gang. When a police officer went to the Kelly home to arrest Dan, a fight broke out between them. The officer was hurt during the struggle, and Mrs. Kelly helped bandage him up. But the officer was too upset to be grateful. He arrested not only Dan, but Mrs. Kelly too! Ned offered to give himself up if the police would let his mother go. When the police said no, Ned was furious. He wanted revenge.

A few months later, the police decided to go after the Kelly Gang again. At this time, the gang was hiding in the mountains, and the police could not capture them. Now they were truly outlaws.

The Last Stand

Over the years, the Kelly Gang continued to rob banks, but they never hurt regular citizens. Many local people gave them food and a place to hide. In 1880, Ned and his gang came up with a plan to set up their own government. However, the police soon cornered the gang in a hotel. It would be the Kelly Gang's last stand. Ned was wounded and the rest of the gang was killed.

Ned Kelly was hanged for his crimes a few months later. He was only twenty-five years old. However, his story of crime and injustice has lived a much longer life.

Ned Kelly wore this homemade armor in the last stand.

WANTED

Cheng I Sao

CRIME: Robbery at sea

Fearless Female

Pirates are the thieves of the sea, attacking ships and stealing their goods. There were thousands of pirates in the waters around China about 200 years ago. One of the best known Chinese pirates was a woman, Cheng I Sao [Cheng – YEE – sow]. Many call her the Queen of Pirates.

How did a woman become a pirate? She married one. Cheng I Sao's husband made her a commander of one of his ships. Together, they united all of the Chinese pirates into one giant fleet. This fleet included 400 ships and 70,000 pirates.

Cheng I Sao's husband died in 1804, and she took over the fleet. Because Cheng I Sao was a strong, fair leader, the pirates respected her. Though her punishments were harsh, she only punished pirates who disobeyed the rules. She always paid the pirates their fair share of the riches they stole.

The Chinese navy tried constantly to overcome the pirates. But Cheng I Sao was a fearless fighter. This made her pirates fearless, too. They captured the navy ships and made their fleet even bigger.

A Chinese pirate ship attacks a trade ship.

After years of fighting, the navy offered the pirate fleet a deal. If Cheng I Sao and her fleet would give up pirating, the navy would pardon them for their crimes and leave them alone. The navy even invited the pirates to join the military! Cheng I Sao agreed to the deal. In 1810, she retired from pirating as a wealthy woman. Some call her the most successful pirate ever to live.

Practice the Skill

Cause and Effect: Chain Reactions

1. Look at paragraph 3 on page 46. Fill in the chart to show what happened when the sheriff tried to capture Robin Hood.

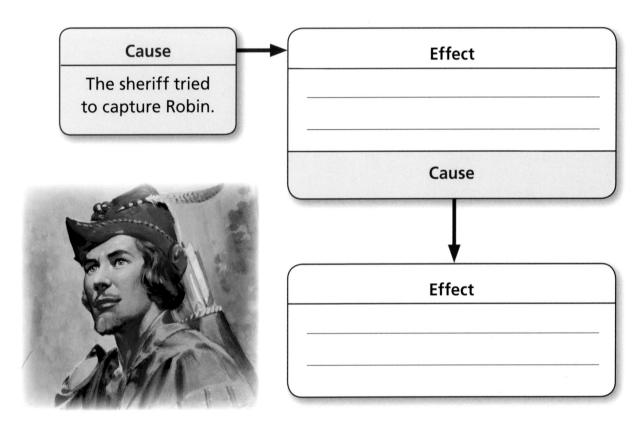

Cause
The sheriff tried to capture Robin.

→

Effect
_____
_____
Cause

↓

Effect
_____
_____

2. Look at the first paragraph on page 47. What was the result of more and more people joining Robin Hood's cause?

_____

_____

Check Comprehension

What did the Sheriff of Nottingham do with the taxes he collected?

_____

_____

Freedom Fighter or Criminal?

What happened when a police officer went to arrest Dan Kelly? Describe a chain of three events.

A Pirate's Life

1. What did Cheng I Sao do when her husband died?

_____

2. Cheng I Sao finally agreed to give up pirating. Write two effects of this decision.

- _____
- _____

Vocabulary

What does the word *commit* mean on page 47?

_____

Writing

Robin Hood was a thief. Why is he still considered a hero in our culture? Explain.

PROMETHEUS THE TRICKSTER

THE GREEK GOD PROMETHEUS HAD A TOUGH ASSIGNMENT FROM HIS KING, ZEUS—TO CREATE HUMANS.

What traits should I give humans?

HIS BROTHER EPIMETHEUS HAD AN EASIER TASK—TO CREATE ANIMALS.

I'll give animals courage, speed, strength, cunning, and a protective covering.

SO EPIMETHEUS USED ALL THE GOOD TRAITS. PROMETHEUS DIDN'T HAVE MANY OPTIONS.

I guess I'll make humans look like gods.

ZEUS HEARD WHAT PROMETHEUS HAD DONE.

How dare you make humans look like gods?! Now you must sacrifice an ox to me.

PROMETHEUS SACRIFICED AN OX, BUT HE WAS A TRICKSTER.

I will put the parts into two piles—good and bad. I'll make sure he chooses the bad pile.

IT WAS HARD TO FOOL ZEUS, BUT PROMETHEUS DID IT. ZEUS WANTED TO PUNISH HIM.

Now your humans shall never have the secret of fire!

PROMETHEUS WAS WORRIED. HE WENT TO THE HALL OF THE GODS TO THINK OF A PLAN.

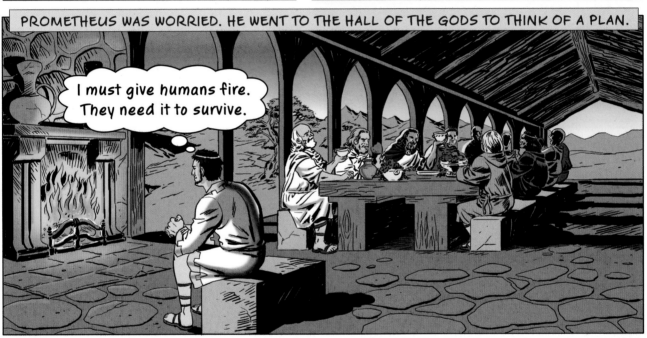

I must give humans fire. They need it to survive.

PROMETHEUS WAITED FOR THE HALL TO EMPTY. THEN HE PUT HIS PLAN INTO ACTION.

I hope humans are grateful for this...

Prometheus the Trickster **53**

PROMETHEUS SHOWED HUMANS HOW FIRE COULD BE USED TO KEEP THEM WARM AND COOK THEIR FOOD.

ZEUS WAS FURIOUS WHEN HE FOUND OUT.

Because of what you've done, humans can become gods! I will punish you for this!

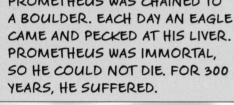

PROMETHEUS WAS CHAINED TO A BOULDER. EACH DAY AN EAGLE CAME AND PECKED AT HIS LIVER. PROMETHEUS WAS IMMORTAL, SO HE COULD NOT DIE. FOR 300 YEARS, HE SUFFERED.

FINALLY, PROMETHEUS'S FRIEND HERCULES RESCUED HIM. PROMETHEUS WAS FREE!

I fear Zeus will find other ways to punish me now.

Cause and Effect

1. Look at page 52. Fill in the chart to show the chain of events.

Cause
Epimetheus took all the good traits.

→

Effect

Cause

↓

Effect

2. Look at page 53. Explain why Zeus will not allow humans to have the secret of fire.

_____

_____

_____

Check Comprehension

1. Look at page 54. According to Zeus, why would humans one day become gods?

_____

2. Who freed Prometheus?

_____

Outside the Box

What was the result of Pandora opening the wedding gift?

Vocabulary

1. Write the meanings of these words.

   • assignment (page 52) _____

   • sacrifice (page 52) _____

2. Use each word in a sentence that shows its meaning.

   • cunning (page 52) _____

   _____

   • immortal (page 54) _____

   _____

Writing

Explain how Athena's gift helped humans.

Text Connections

You have read several texts about crime and punishment. Now choose one of the following topics to investigate.

🔨 Write a short story about someone who is punished for something he or she didn't do.

🔨 In small groups, discuss this statement: "Schools must have rules for students." Select someone from each group to present the group's arguments to the class.

🔨 Write a poem about Robin Hood, Ned Kelly, or Cheng I Sao.

🔨 Jesse James was an outlaw in the Wild West. Working with a partner, research some of his adventures. What crimes did he commit and why? How did he become a legend? Present your findings to the class on a "Wanted" poster.

🔨 Research another Greek god and create a comic strip about one of his or her adventures.

🔨 Write a humorous story about a chain reaction. Start with the words, "I dropped my pencil on the floor." Be clear about how one event leads to the next event, which leads to the next event, and so on.

Continue your explorations by reading these books:

Incredible Crimes by Linda Atkinson
Extra, extra, read all about it! Learn about these amazing crimes—and what happened when the criminals were caught.

Really, Truly, Everything's Fine by Linda Leopold Strauss
Jill's world crumbles when her father is accused of a crime. Will anything ever be fine again?

True Escape Stories by Paul Dowswell
Read eight true stories about men who risked their lives to escape from prisons around the world.

What Is a Hero?

* A baby boy is left on a doorstep. Find out how he would become the king of Britain.

* Ms. Jenkins is an excellent music teacher. So why is she about to lose her job?

* A talented young nurse helps doctors research a cure for yellow fever—at great cost.

Unit 4

Making Inferences To make inferences, use what is suggested but not stated directly in a text to better understand characters and events.

KING ARTHUR:
THE SWORD IN THE STONE

> **What kind of person was Arthur? Would he make a good king?**

Long ago in Britain, there lived a great and powerful king named Arthur. He is the hero of many stories and legends from the Middle Ages. With his Knights of the Round Table at his side, Arthur brought peace to Britain. This is the tale of how he became king.

When he was just a baby, Arthur was left on the doorstep of Sir Ector, a knight who decided to take him in. "I will raise him with my own son, Kay," Sir Ector said, "and Kay will be like an older brother to him."

Arthur spent his childhood doing whatever Kay wanted. "Fetch my horse!" ordered Kay. "Get me those apples! Clean my boots!"

Young Arthur was happy to obey. As a reward, he got to watch Kay train to be a knight. He loved seeing Kay ride his horse, swing his sword, and shoot his bow and arrow.

Arthur liked to practice using Kay's heavy sword. Kay laughed and said, "You can barely swing that sword! You'll never be a knight." Arthur just smiled.

~ ⚜ ~

When Kay was old enough, he entered a tournament planned for all of Britain. The event was a day of combat. Knights fought against other knights to decide who was the strongest. But that was not the only reason for the tournament. Britain was without a king. The winner of the tournament would be crowned king.

Kay worked hard to prepare for the great contest. He became more and more excited as the day drew near.

Arthur was excited, too. He had never been to such an event before. He couldn't wait to watch the knights in combat. But Kay had other ideas. "You'll be my squire," he said. "You'll take care of my horse and armor and weapons. And you'll make sure I have all I need."

"Of course, Kay," said Arthur.

"*Sir* Kay to you, now," said Kay. "You're my squire, remember?"

Sir Ector, Kay, and Arthur traveled to London for the tournament. The city was so full they had to stay at an inn a long way from the tournament grounds. As they walked to the event, Arthur noticed a strange monument in the middle of a marketplace. It was a large stone with a sword stuck in it. Arthur glanced at it as they walked, but he was too weighed down with Kay's armor and weapons to get a good look.

At the tournament grounds, Arthur helped Kay put on his armor. "Now, hand me my sword," said Kay.

Arthur looked around. "Sword? Where is his sword?" he thought. "I seem to have forgotten your sword, Sir Kay," Arthur said nervously. "I was sure I had brought it with me!"

Kay let out a bellow and gave Arthur a menacing look. "I can't fight without a sword!" he yelled. "Go back to the inn and get it. And be back before I have to fight, or I'll have your ears!"

Arthur ran as fast as he could. He began to panic because there wasn't enough time to get to the inn. "Sir Kay must have a sword!" thought Arthur. As he ran past the strange monument again, Arthur stopped in his tracks. "A sword!" he cried. "Surely that will do!"

Arthur stepped in front of the stone, seized the sword's handle, and pulled. The sword slid out of the stone like a hot knife through butter.

Arthur ran all the way back to the tournament and thrust the sword into Kay's hand just in time. "Here you go, Sir Kay," said Arthur, panting.

Sir Ector's eyes grew wide when he saw the sword. "Wait!" he cried. "Where did you get that sword?"

Kay shrugged. "Arthur brought it," he said. "He forgot to bring mine."

"Arthur," said Sir Ector, turning to his adopted son, "where did you get that sword?"

Arthur hung his head. "I borrowed it," he said softly, "from the stone in the marketplace. I'll put it back, I promise." He looked up. "What—what are you doing?"

Sir Ector had fallen to his knees. "My king," he said. Sir Ector turned to Kay. "Kneel to your king," he ordered.

Sir Ector showed the stunned Arthur the writing carved on the sword: "Whoever draws this sword shall be king of Britain."

"Many have tried," Sir Ector said. "But only you have done it."

Arthur could hardly believe it, but it was true. Only a true heir to the British throne could have pulled out the sword. The tournament was stopped immediately—Britain had found its king.

Practice the Skill

Making Inferences

1. Read the information below. What inference can you make about Sir Ector?

Information	Inference
• Sir Ector took Arthur in. • He raised Arthur with his own son, Kay.	_____ _____ _____

2. Write two pieces of information from page 62 that support the inference below.

   Arthur didn't know what it meant to pull the sword from the stone.

   • _____

   • _____

Check Comprehension

1. What does a squire do?

   _____

   _____

2. According to the story, what were two ways one could become the King of Britain?

   • _____

   • _____

Vocabulary

Write the meanings of these words.

• combat (page 61) _____

• bellow (page 61) _____

• menacing (page 61) _____

Saving the Music

How did Ms. Jenkins help the band live its dream?

LATE FRIDAY EVENING . . .

PANAMA CLUB

What a set! Let's hear it again for Cloudy Forecast!

AN UNEXPECTED VISITOR APPROACHES THE STAGE.

Ms. Jenkins? Is it really you?

I can't believe you remember me!

Remember you?! You're our hero!

The best music teacher ever! I can't believe you're here.

You're the reason we're living this dream.

You're all so kind—and talented!

AFTER THE CONCERT, THE MUSICIANS TELL THEIR FORMER TEACHER ABOUT LIFE ON THE ROAD. BUT THEY ALSO WANT TO KNOW WHAT SHE'S BEEN UP TO.

Tell us about your latest crop of musicians!

Any rock stars in the making?

Ms. Jenkins, is something wrong?

It's nothing. It's just that...

MS. JENKINS DESCRIBES THE NEW BUDGET CUTS AT VALLEY VIEW JUNIOR HIGH. AS IT TURNED OUT, MUSIC WAS THE FIRST THING TO GO.

Making Inferences

1. Read the information below. What inference can you make about Ms. Jenkins?

Information

Inference

- Maggie says, "You're our hero."

- Violet says, "The best music teacher ever!"

- Raleigh says, "You're the reason we're living this dream!"

_____

_____

_____

_____

2. What do you think Ms. Jenkins cares more about — losing her job or the students not having music class?

_____

Write three examples from the text that support your answer.

- _____

- _____

- _____

Check Comprehension

What is the main reason Cloudy Forecast plays a concert at the school?

_____

_____

_____

After the Concert

1. The concert brought in a lot of money. So why were the band members unhappy?

   _____

   _____

2. Look at the last panel on page 67. What leads Ms. Jenkins to think that the fight is just beginning?

   _____

   _____

Vocabulary

1. Define these words as they are used in the text.

   • crop (page 64) _____

   • draws (page 66) _____

2. Use each phrase in a sentence that shows its meaning.

   • budget cuts (page 65) _____

   _____

   • media frenzy (page 66) _____

   _____

Writing

Think about how the members of Cloudy Forecast feel about Ms. Jenkins. Do you think Ms. Jenkins feels the same way about them? Explain.

Courageous Americans

http://www.claramaass.com/feverfighter/

🏠 Home 🔍 Search

What kind of person was Clara Maass?

Clara Maass

Nurse Clara Maass was only twenty-five when she died of yellow fever in 1901. How did she catch this deadly disease? She caught it by choice. Some people call her a hero because of it. Why did she make that choice? Read on for the answers.

Clara's Early Years

Clara Maass was born in New Jersey in 1876. Her parents were from Germany. They sometimes had trouble finding work in the United States. As the oldest of ten children, young Clara had to grow up fast. She gave almost all of the money she made from an after-school job to her parents.

When she was not in school or at work, Maass's main interest was medicine. After finishing high school in just three years, she applied to a local nursing program. She was three years younger than most applicants, but she still got accepted. In 1898, Newark German Hospital in New Jersey named her head nurse. Maass was just twenty-one years old.

A Frightening Fever

Maass did not stay in her job for very long. In that same year, she volunteered as an army nurse. The United States was at war with Spain. She was soon sent to Cuba, where much of the fighting was taking place.

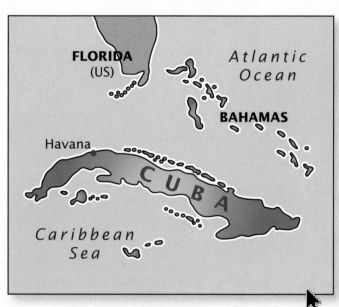

Cuba is about 90 miles from the United States.

Maass's nursing skills were put to good use. But she was not treating soldiers who were wounded in battle. Most of them were sick with a strange disease. The disease took away their strength. It gave them pounding headaches and high fevers. It turned their skin and eyes a sickly yellow.
People called the disease "yellow fever."

Some soldiers recovered quickly, but others were not so lucky. Thousands of soldiers died from yellow fever during the war. Since there was no cure, Maass could only comfort the stricken soldiers as best she could before they died. It was Maass's first encounter with yellow fever, but it would not be her last.

The Research Begins

Doctors knew very little about yellow fever. They were sure the soldiers caught it in the Cuban jungles, but how? Did some animal in the jungle give it to them? And how did it spread so quickly? The army doctors were frustrated. How could they stop this disease if they didn't know how people got it? That soon changed.

In 1900, the U.S. Army set up a research station in Cuba. The goal of the research was to find out what caused yellow fever. If doctors could find its cause, maybe they could find its cure. When Maass heard about the research, she wrote to Major Gorgas, the person in charge. Could she help? The major wrote back, telling her to come immediately.

Clara Maass (third from right) at an army base in Jacksonville, Florida, just before departing for Cuba

The doctors had made great progress in their research. By the time Maass arrived in Cuba, they were almost certain that people caught yellow fever from mosquitoes. The Cuban jungles were infested with them. Doctors believed the mosquitoes infected soldiers with their bite.

Mosquitoes spread yellow fever.

The doctors needed proof. Unfortunately, there was only one way for them to get it. They would have to expose healthy people to infected mosquitoes. If the exposed people caught yellow fever, then the doctors would know that the mosquitoes were carrying the disease.

A Deadly Experiment

The doctors began asking for volunteers. Maass, along with eighteen others, agreed to be infected. They were each given $100 for the risky experiment. Maass sent every penny of it to her family back home. In February 1901, the experiments began.

At first it looked like the doctors were wrong. Over the next six months, just one person caught a mild case of yellow fever. Then in August, seven volunteers came down with the disease, including Maass. She soon got better, but the worst was yet to come.

The doctors had believed that since Maass had survived yellow fever already, she would be immune to the disease, unable to catch it again. To test this, Maass would have to be bitten again. Once again, she agreed to do it.

Maass received her final bite on August 14, 1901. She soon fell ill. She was given the best care possible, but it was not enough. She died of yellow fever just ten days later.

http://www.claramaass.com/feverfighter/

Life After Clara Maass

Maass's death shocked doctors and the American public. She was the only American, and the only woman, to die from the experiment. Many were outraged at what the doctors had done to her and the other volunteers. Her death upset so many people that the government soon banned all experiments on humans.

Clara Maass did not die in vain, however. Tests finally proved that mosquitoes carried yellow fever. Years later, doctors created a shot that protected against it. There is still no cure for the disease, but it is now easily prevented. Thanks to Maass's sacrifice, death from yellow fever is rare.

Clara Maass was honored on a 1976 U.S. postage stamp.

Front page of the *New York Journal* August 26, 1901

Maass's sacrifice has been recognized in many ways. In 1952, the hospital she trained at changed its name to the Clara Maass Memorial Hospital. Today it is called the Clara Maass Medical Center. There is also a school and a hospital named after her in Cuba. In 1976, one hundred years after she was born, Maass's face appeared on a United States postage stamp. She was the first nurse ever to receive this honor.

Was Clara Maass a fool who threw away her life at a young age? Or was she a hero who risked her life to save others? That is for you to decide. One thing is for sure, her sacrifice will always be remembered.

Practice the Skill

Making Inferences

1. Look at the first paragraph of Clara's Early Years. What inference can you make from the information below?

Information	Inference
• Clara's parents had trouble finding work. • There were ten children in the family. • Clara gave almost all the money she made from an after-school job to her parents.	_____ _____ _____ _____

2. Look at the rest of Clara's Early Years. What inference can you make from the fact that Maass was named head nurse?

_____

_____

Check Comprehension

1. Why did the U.S. Army set up a research station in Cuba?

_____

_____

2. Why did the United States government ban all experiments on humans?

_____

_____

Maass's Legacy

Write three facts from page 73 that support the inference below.

**People in the United States and Cuba felt
it was important to honor Clara Maass.**

- _____
  _____

- _____
  _____

- _____
  _____

Vocabulary

1. Define the following words as they are used in the text.

   - progress (page 72) _____

   - infested (page 72) _____

   - volunteers (page 72) _____

2. Find the phrase "die in vain" on page 73. Explain what it means.

   _____

   _____

Writing

Why do you think Clara Maass did what she did? Write your opinion
and give reasons.

Text Connections

Now that you have read several texts about different kinds of heroes, choose one of the following topics to investigate.

* Think about the heroes you've read about in this unit. Discuss the topic "What is a hero?" with a partner. Write a list of the traits and actions that you think a hero should display. Share your list with your classmates and see if they agree.

* Find out more about the legend of King Arthur and the Knights of the Round Table. Who were Sir Lancelot and Sir Galahad? What were their stories? Choose one story and write it as a comic strip.

* Research legendary heroes from different cultures. You might start by looking into Greek, Roman, or Native American myths. Choose your favorite story and tell it to the class.

* Write an essay about someone who has made a big difference in your life. What traits does that person have? What has he or she done that you admire? Explain with examples.

* Find a recent, real-life hero story in the newspaper or on a news Web site. Write an article that retells the story in your own words.

* Research and write a report on the life of another hero of science or medicine, such as Clara Barton, founder of the Red Cross.

Continue your explorations by reading these books:

I Never Wanted to Be Famous by Eth Clifford
Newspaper headlines call Goody Tribble a hero. Can he live up to the title?

Rescue! True Stories of the Winners of the Young American Medal for Bravery by Walter R. Brown and Norman D. Anderson
These young people risked their lives to save their friends, family, or neighbors—and earned a medal in the process.

Ryan and Jimmy and the Well in Africa That Brought Them Together by Herb Shoveller
When Ryan heard that people in Africa don't have safe drinking water, he wanted to help. How much difference can one kid make?

How I See It

* Friendship can be described in many different ways. What does friendship mean to you?

* Stay tuned for the greatest baseball game of the season. Which star players will outshine the rest?

* If you've got issues, Dr. Dave has all the answers. But is his advice any good?

Figurative Language Figurative language is the use of similes, metaphors, and personification to create vivid descriptions.

Through Thick and Thin

How does the figurative language used in these poems help describe friendship?

Friendship is like china
Costly and rare.
Tho' it can be mended
The scratches are always there.

Author unknown

Misery is when your
very best friend
calls you a name she really
didn't mean to call you at all.

Misery is when you call
your very best friend a name
you didn't mean to call her, either.

Langston Hughes

My Hard Repair Job

In the awful quarrel
we had, my temper burnt
our friendship to cinders.
How can I make it whole again?

This way, that way,
that time, this time,
I pick up the burnt bits,
trying to change them back.

James Berry

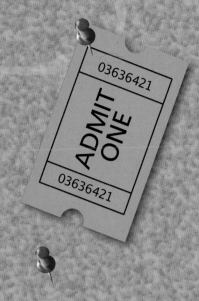

ADMIT ONE

03636421

03636421

Friendship

There is a secret thread that makes us friends
    Turn away from hard and breakful eyes
    Turn away from cold and painful lies
That speaks of other, more important ends
There are two hard but tender hearts that beat
    Take always my hand at special times
    Take always my dark and precious rhymes
That sing so brightly when our glad souls meet

Walter Dean Myers

my friend

my friend is
like bark
rounding a tree

he warms
like sun
on a winter day

he cools
like water
in the hot noon

his voice
is ready
as a spring bird

he is
my friend
and I
am his

Emily Hearn

Practice the Skill

Figurative Language

The chart below lists examples of figurative language from the poems on pages 78–79. Write the meaning of each sentence and the type of figurative language.

Figurative Language	Meaning	Type of Figurative Language
Friendship is like china.		
Misery is when your very best friend calls you a name.		
My temper burnt our friendship to cinders.		

Check Comprehension

How does the author of "my friend" feel about her friend? Explain in your own words.

_____

_____

_____

Vocabulary

Write the meanings of these words.

- mended (page 78) _____

- cinders (page 79) _____

- precious (page 80) _____

LIVE FROM THE COMMENTARY BOX

How does the figurative language used by Jimmy and Denise help listeners to enjoy the game more?

VOICE-OVER: Today's baseball game between the Hillview Hurlers and the Silver Valley Sluggers is brought to you by Homer's House of Hot Dogs. Their hot dogs are a home run! And now, live from Mesa Ballpark at Hillview High, here's Jimmy Styles and Denise Deluca!

Jimmy: Hey there, baseball fans, Jimmy Styles here.

Denise: And I'm Denise Deluca. It's a beautiful afternoon in Hillview! The sun is smiling down on two of the best teams in the league. Today's game promises to be a classic. Right, Jimmy?

Jimmy: That's right, Denise. Every game between these teams is a cliff-hanger. You never know what's going to happen! Now for a look at today's starting pitchers. We have Frankie "Fastball" Fernando, the Hurlers' number one pitcher. This kid has an arm like a cannon!

Denise: And don't forget the Sluggers, Jimmy. Today, they hand the ball to Dan "The Man" Pulaski, who throws every pitch in the book—fastball, curveball, knuckleball, slider. With those weapons, Pulaski could be a strike-out machine!

Jimmy: The game is about to begin. The Hurlers are taking the field as the Sluggers get ready to bat. Leading off for the Sluggers is Bobby "Flash" Braxton. He moves like lightning on the base paths. If he gets on base, expect him to steal.

Denise: Well said, Jimmy. It looks like Fernando is about to throw his first pitch. He winds up, and . . . it's right down the heart of the plate! Strike one.

Jimmy: No swing! Fernando blew that one right by him.

Denise: Fernando throws again, and . . . swing and a miss. Strike two! Fernando's electric today! Braxton looks like a deer in headlights.

Jimmy: Hurlers fans are coming alive now. I've never heard them this loud! They're looking for the strikeout.

Denise: Fernando winds up again, and . . . he strikes Braxton out on just three pitches! The home crowd got what they wanted, Jimmy!

Jimmy: Let's see if Fernando can keep it going against the Sluggers' next batter, first baseman Joey Cole.

Denise: That won't be easy, Jimmy. Cole doesn't hit a lot of home runs, but he always seems to find a way to get on base. Cole steps into the batter's box. Fernando throws and . . . Cole hits it foul and out of play. Strike one.

Jimmy: That was a healthy swing by Cole.

Denise: Fernando is ready to throw again. His next pitch is . . . way inside! Cole had to duck to get out of the way.

Jimmy: Sometimes his pitches have a mind of their own. Let's see if he can recover with this next one.

Denise: Fernando throws and . . . Cole hits it deep to right field. Right fielder Jin Suzuki runs back, back, back, he jumps up, and . . . he makes the catch at the edge of the wall! Wow! What a catch! The crowd is going wild!

Jimmy: Suzuki is like an acrobat out there in right field! He had to time that jump perfectly to make the catch. Fernando is lucky to have Suzuki playing behind him. That ball would've been a home run!

Denise: That's two quick outs for Fernando in the top of the first inning. The score is tied 0–0. Now at bat is Rocky Dunn, the Slugger's star hitter.

Jimmy: Dunn leads the league in home runs. He's been on fire lately, hitting a home run in each of his last five games. Let's see if he can keep that streak going.

Denise: Dunn stands in against Fernando, and the first pitch is inside. Ball one. That one almost hit Dunn!

Jimmy: Dunn shoots Fernando an icy stare. It looks like he won't be intimidated by Fernando.

Denise: Fernando's second pitch is a strike on the outside corner. There's now one ball and one strike on Dunn.

Jimmy: You can feel the tension growing during this at-bat, Denise. The crowd's cheers are getting louder . . .

Denise: Fernando is ready to throw again. Here's the windup and the pitch. Dunn swings, and . . . he hits it deep to right field. It's going way back! That ball shot off his bat like a rocket!

Jimmy: And it's another home run for Dunn! He just can't be stopped. It seems as if Fernando is unraveling a bit here. This game is still young, though, so he has time to pull himself together.

Denise: Fernando's job won't get any easier, though, Jimmy. Up next for the Sluggers is the catcher, Andre Greene. Fernando rears back to throw, and . . . Greene fouls it off for strike one.

Jimmy: Another fastball from Fernando. He's like a broken record, throwing fastball after fastball.

Denise: Well, now we know how he got his nickname! Fernando's second pitch is low and away, and now there's one ball and one strike on Greene.

Jimmy: I don't know how Hurlers catcher Dave Beck was able to get a hold of that fastball. He must have flypaper fingers!

Denise: No doubt, Jimmy. That was a nice grab by Beck. Fernando throws again. Greene swings and hits it to the shortstop, Sam Kline. Kline throws to first, and Greene is out! Greene wasn't even close to the base.

Jimmy: No, he wasn't, Denise. Greene is about as fast as a turtle on the base paths. There was no way he would beat out that throw and get in safely.

Denise: So, at the bottom of the first inning, it's Sluggers 1, Hurlers 0. Now we'll see how Sluggers pitcher Dan Pulaski does against this tough Hurlers offense. This is shaping up to be a great game.

Jimmy: It sure is, Denise. Stay tuned for the bottom of the first. We'll be right back after a word from our sponsor.

Practice the Skill

Figurative Language

1. The chart below lists examples of figurative language on page 82. Write the meaning of each sentence and the type of figurative language.

Figurative Language	Meaning	Type of Figurative Language
Their hot dogs are a home run!		
The sun is smiling.		
This kid has an arm like a cannon!		
Braxton looks like a deer in headlights.		

2. Look at the fifth paragraph on page 82. Why does Denise describe Pulaski's pitches as "weapons"?

_____

3. What does "it's right down the heart of the plate" mean?

_____

Check Comprehension

What usually happens once Bobby "Flash" Braxton gets on base?

_____

Top of the First

1. Write an example of figurative language from pages 83–85 that describes each player's actions. Then write the meaning of each example.

Suzuki

Figurative Language: _____

Meaning: _____

Dunn

Figurative Language: _____

Meaning: _____

Fernando

Figurative Language: _____

Meaning: _____

2. What does "the game is still young" mean on page 84?

_____

Vocabulary

Define these words as they are used in the text.

- recover (page 83) _____

- intimidated (page 84) _____

- tension (page 84) _____

Writing

The broadcast ended just before the Hurlers came to bat. Imagine that in the second half of the first inning the Hurlers tie the game 1–1. Write the dialogue for Denise and Jimmy as they describe what happens. Use figurative language.

ASK Dr. Dave

How does figurative language help you to understand these teen problems?

Dear Dr. Dave,

I really need your help. There's a girl in my class who is ruining my life. I know she hates me, but I have no idea why! I've never done anything to her. She's a real snake, and I know she's the one who started all the rumors about me last week. Nothing she said was true, but it doesn't matter. No one at school will talk to me now—not even my best friend.

This week she stopped spreading rumors. At first I was relieved, but now she's calling me names. Yesterday she said my hair was like a pile of cooked spaghetti—stringy and limp! Everyone burst out laughing, and I'm sure my face turned as red as a lobster.

My stomach was killing me this morning when I got up, and I really didn't want to go to school. But my mom didn't believe me when I said I was sick. She just told me to keep smiling and promised things would get better. But when I got to school, there was a picture on my locker door. It was a sumo wrestler's body with my face pasted on it. I wanted to crawl under a rock.

I feel like giving up and changing schools. What should I do?

Yours truly,
Friendless and Hopeless

Dear Friendless,

You may feel friendless, but you shouldn't feel hopeless! You just need to know how to respond to a bully. I know, I know—you're going to tell me that this girl hasn't tried to beat you up, so she isn't a bully. But there are different kinds of bullies. Some bullies are violent, and others stick to more passive methods of bullying, like name-calling.

Most bullies just want to be the queen bee or king of the hill. They want attention—any kind of attention. If you can ignore her, she won't get the attention she wants.

The next step is to try to be strong. Think of someone brave, like Rosa Parks or Mahatma Gandhi, who inspires you. Be as courageous and as tough as that person. Tell this girl to stop making fun of you.

Sometimes it helps to get someone else involved. For example, call up that best friend of yours. Explain to her that the rumors aren't true, and tell her you need her support. She should be able to help you out. If she can be your rock, it will be harder for the bully to make fun of you.

Dealing with a bully is never easy, but changing schools is not the answer. By taking the right steps, you can stop this bully in her tracks!

Good luck!

Dr. Dave

Dear Dr. Dave,

I can't believe I'm writing to you, but I really don't know what else to do. I want to get an after-school job, but my parents won't let me! We fight about it all the time. I just want to be independent, you know? All my friends have jobs, and they have money to go to the movies or to the mall. I always have to ask my parents for money, and they question me like I'm a criminal! They want to know where I'm going and what I'm doing. If they don't like my answers, they won't give me the money.

You would think that my parents would want me to get a job. They constantly talk about money disappearing like snow in July. But they still won't let me earn any! They're always complaining about my grades. My grades could be better, but so what? What do my grades have to do with anything?

I wish I could explain to my parents why it's so important to me to get a job. But sometimes they just don't listen. When we argue, my heart jumps up and down in my chest and my voice gets shaky. Just thinking about it all makes my head spin! I really need your advice, Dr. Dave. What should I do?

Sincerely,

Sick of Whining

Dear Sick of Whining,

This problem is much more common than you think. Teens often want to be independent, and parents aren't always happy about that. Teens and their parents can be stubborn mules when they want to be! But you can learn to compromise with your parents.

There are a couple things you can do to help yourself stay as cool as a cucumber. Take a deep breath before you answer your parents' questions. Try not to get impatient or upset. If you stay calm, you'll be able to think logically and argue your point of view more clearly. Think about your parents' point of view, and answer each concern they have.

Parents want their kids to be responsible, mature, and trustworthy. Do you recall a time when you took care of a younger sibling or you helped a friend with a difficult problem? Sharing one of these stories with your parents will show them you've been thinking like an adult and you're ready for more responsibility.

Since your parents are concerned about your grades, that's the place to start. Tell your parents that you'll bring up your grades. Then ask if you can get a job when your grades improve.

Just remember, if your parents agree to this plan, you'll have to work like a dog to keep your grades up! But you'll have a job and your own money, and your parents' hearts will sing with pride.

Good luck!

Dr. Dave

Figurative Language

1. Read Friendless and Hopeless's letter on page 88. Fill in the chart with examples of figurative language she uses.

Figurative Language	Meaning	Type of Figurative Language
		metaphor
		simile
		simile

2. Read these metaphors from page 89. What does each one mean?

- Most bullies just want to be the queen bee or king of the hill.

   Meaning: _____

   _____

- She can be your rock.

   Meaning: _____

   _____

Check Comprehension

According to Dr. Dave, what are the two kinds of bullies?

_____

_____

To Work or Not To Work

1. Read these similes from the letters on pages 90–91. What does each one mean?

Sick of Whining

"They talk about money disappearing like snow in July."

_____

_____

_____

Dr. Dave

"Youll have to work like a dog."

_____

_____

_____

2. Both Sick of Whining and Dr. Dave use personification in the final paragraph of their letters. Write one example from each letter.

- _____
- _____

Vocabulary

Use each word in a sentence that shows its meaning.

- rumors (page 88) _____

_____

- independent (page 90) _____

_____

Writing

Suppose Dr. Dave thinks that students should *not* have after-school jobs. Write a new response to Sick of Whining. Use figurative language.

Text Connections

You have read several texts about teen life and interests. Now choose one of the following topics that interests *you*.

* Write your own poem about friendship. Try to use at least one example of simile, metaphor, and personification.

* Look in poetry books to find poems that use figurative language to create vivid images. Illustrate your favorite poem and share it with the class.

* With a partner, find descriptions of sporting events from newspaper columns or magazines. Highlight examples of figurative language and share them with the class.

* Create a comic strip about an exciting event in your life. Include illustrations, dialogue, and text boxes. Use figurative language.

* Use the Internet to research the pros and cons of teens having after-school jobs. Create a poster to present your findings to the class.

* Work with a partner or in a small group to create your own advice column. Write letters and responses in the style of *Ask Dr. Dave*.

Continue your explorations by reading these books:

Backstage at a Movie Set by Katherine Wessling
Do you dream of acting in or directing a movie? This book will tell you how!

I Was a Teenage Professional Wrestler by Ted Lewin
Explore the wrestling world through the eyes of Ted Lewin: art student by day, professional wrestler by night.

Love That Dog by Sharon Creech
Jack's poems don't rhyme. He doesn't even think they're poems—but are they?

Modern Media

▶▶ One critic loves the movie. One hates it. Which critic is the most convincing?

▶▶ Television, computers, video games, music—are they bad for your health? You decide!

▶▶ People download their favorite music and movies from the Internet all the time. But should they have to pay?

Unit 6

Recognizing Viewpoint: Persuasion To evaluate persuasive writing, see if it is fair, logical, and supported by facts.

Dueling Movie Reviews

How do these reviewers try to persuade their readers?

Born to Be a Winner

by ANGIE FORBES

Rating: ★ ★ ★ ★ ★ Staff Writer

Small-town Tale Does Not Disappoint

This time next year, Steve Fielding may well be stepping on stage at the Academy Awards to pick up the Oscar for Best Director. His latest film, *Born to Be Wild*, is that good.

Born to Be Wild is set in a small midwestern town. It tells the story of a young man named Brad, who longs to make it big in a city, any city. On one occasion, Brad buys a one-way bus ticket to New York. He never boards. Another time, he thinks about taking a cab to the airport and then flying to L.A. He walks to the edge of the town and eventually takes a cab—back home. One thing always holds Brad back—fear of failure!

Brad's wholesome, help-your-neighbor reputation has turned him into a hometown hero. What his family and friends don't know is that Brad feels trapped. Will Brad give up his local celebrity status to achieve greater things elsewhere? Audiences will relate to Brad's small-town struggle.

Stellar Performances

Steve Fielding has brought out the best in his cast. James Anderson is superb as the brooding Brad. Anderson's earlier movies were all flops. No doubt he drew on his Utah upbringing to play Brad so convincingly.

Tricia Ross is just as believable. She plays Nadine, Brad's quirky, on-and-off love interest. During the making of *Born to Be Wild*, there were rumors that Anderson and Ross did not see eye-to-eye. If that's the case, Fielding has done an amazing job to ensure that the off-screen emotions remained exactly that—off the screen.

Members of the supporting cast also shine. Margaret Wilde is noble and charming as Brad's mother, Val. Jack Mitchell stands out in his portrayal of Brad's distant and ailing father, Joe. And Simone Sinclair adds some welcome humor as Brad's meddling sister, Sheri.

One very moving scene stands out in my mind. Brad and Joe are having a heated argument about family responsibility. At one point, they both turn to Val, looking for support. Val just can't bear to take sides. There is an awkward pause that seems to go on forever. Then Sheri breaks the tension with an amusing remark that brings everyone back to

earth. Her comment ends the fight, at least for the moment.

See It!

Born to Be Wild is a tender—but not sappy—portrait of American life. It's a story worth knowing, full of performances worth watching. ■

BORED TO BE WILD

by KENNY FLEMMING
Movie Critic

Rating:
Don't waste your time!

Bland Film Offers Nothing New

There is no getting away from the fact that *Born to Be Wild* is a turkey. What I hoped to see was a "coming-of-age" classic, where the lead character finds out what he is really made of. What I got was a weak replay of ten other, better movies. CONTINUED ON NEXT PAGE

Déjà Vu

The characters could have jumped out of *Hit the Road*, a far superior film to this one. Both films have lead male characters desperate to leave home but wary of what lies ahead. However, in *Hit the Road*, director Amy Wu had the courage to let her actors take risks.

In *Born to Be Wild*, director Steve Fielding controls his actors too closely. There's no on-screen excitement or energy. The biggest culprit is James Anderson, who plays the oh-so-boring Brad. Anderson has shown a great deal of talent in previous films, but he doesn't get out of first gear here. Tricia Ross is equally lifeless in her role as Brad's narrow-minded girlfriend, Nadine. Her accent, her clothing, and her dialogue could not have been more unoriginal.

Another "seen it all before" example is the location. If this isn't the same Main Street that was the backdrop for *Burning Up*, then I'll give up reviewing. The only difference is that the street had presence in *Burning Up*. It looked menacing at night and welcoming during the day. In *Born to Be Wild*, it's just another street. Yawn, yawn, and yawn.

My Verdict

This movie is dull because it has a predictable storyline. You've seen it all before. Don't waste your time. ✪

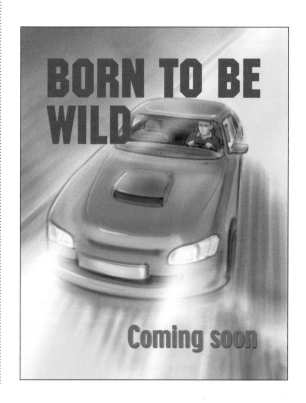

Practice the Skill

Recognizing Viewpoint: Persuasion

1. Below, write each reviewer's viewpoint on *Born to Be Wild*. Then list three reasons or examples they use to support their viewpoints.

Angie Forbes's Viewpoint
_____
_____
Reasons or Examples
• _____   _____
• _____   _____
• _____   _____

Kenny Flemming's Viewpoint
_____
_____
Reasons or Examples
• _____   _____
• _____   _____
• _____   _____

2. Which review do you think is more persuasive? Why?

_____

_____

Vocabulary

1. What is the meaning of *upbringing* on page 96?

_____

2. Write a sentence from page 98 that tells what *predictable* means.

_____

FINDING A BALANCE

by Jake Allen

What do the experts say about young people, media, and exercise?

Pete Tillson

High school freshman Pete Tillson has never felt better. But it wasn't too long ago that he was feeling tired and stressed all the time.

"I couldn't figure it out," said Pete. "After school I'd get on the computer to do homework and maybe play a couple of games. Then I'd watch some TV—you know, like any other normal kid. But I had no energy. Then one day I played a game of soccer with some guys after school," Pete continues. "By the time we were through, I was so sore! But I also felt happy and energized. From that point on, I was hooked on exercise.

"Don't get me wrong—I haven't given up computers and TV," Pete explains. "I just make sure I fit in some kind of physical activity every day."

Luckily Pete was able to work some exercise into his media-filled life. But many kids his age are not. Studies show that teens are spending an average of six hours a day on things like TV, the Internet, music, and video games. With all these media distractions, it seems there's just no time left for kids to stay in shape.

More TVs Than People!

The amount of time young people spend in front of the television has increased over the years. The number of televisions in the United States has increased too. In 1975, most homes had only one television set. Today, there are more TV sets than there are people! Half of homes have three or more TVs. Fifty-four percent of all American school-age children have TVs in their bedrooms. According to the U.S. Census Bureau, in 2006, the average teenager spent the equivalent of sixty-five days in front of the TV!

Where Does the Time Go?

TV, computers, and other digital media all compete for our attention. A 2007 survey found that young people spend a huge amount of time just sitting. They listen to music on their MP3 players, watch DVDs, and send text messages. Many also surf the Internet and play video games. All these activities keep young people from getting enough exercise.

Welcome to the Internet!

The 2007 survey found that the Internet is the second most popular media form, after the TV. It's no wonder that young people in the United States spend an average of twelve hours a week on the Internet. Look at the bar graph below. It provides a picture of how teens spent their time online in 2005.

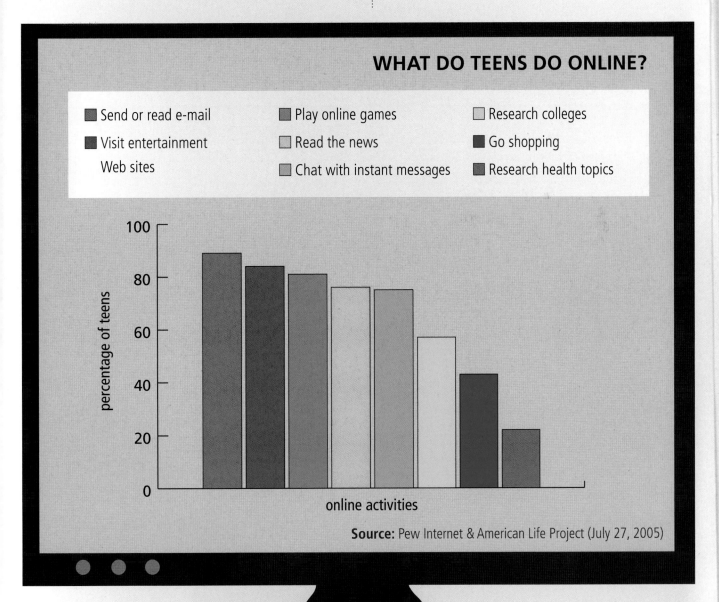

WHAT DO TEENS DO ONLINE?

- Send or read e-mail
- Visit entertainment Web sites
- Play online games
- Read the news
- Chat with instant messages
- Research colleges
- Go shopping
- Research health topics

percentage of teens

online activities

Source: Pew Internet & American Life Project (July 27, 2005)

The Good News

Young people do not have to panic. One expert believes that removing all media from kids' lives is not the answer. According to fitness authority Angela Elliott, "Teens just need to set a cap on the amount of screen time."

But Elliott is quick to point out that not all TV watching is bad. "Some TV time can actually help people to exercise," she says. "Just think of all the exercise DVDs out there today," she says. "You can practice yoga, kickboxing, or hip-hop dancing all from the privacy of your living room. The choices are practically endless.

"There's no law that says children have to sit down when they watch their favorite TV shows, either," she continues. "Walking in place is great exercise. Or you could

Watching TV while exercising is a popular trend.

put a treadmill or an exercise bike in front of the TV."

Elliott explains that some video games even encourage physical activity. In one game, for example, players can get an aerobic workout while performing dance steps. In virtual sports games, players do the same movements they would if they were playing the sport for real. "Video games are no longer just for couch potatoes," she asserts. "With the new exergaming trend, kids can stay fit without even trying."

STEPS YOU CAN TAKE TO FIND A BALANCE

✔ Exercise while listening to your MP3 player.

✔ Use exercise DVDs.

✔ Play virtual dance or sports video games.

✔ Walk on a treadmill or ride an exercise bike while watching TV.

✔ Trade "outside" time for computer time.

"Who says I don't get enough exercise? My eyes have never worked harder."

Logging Off

"Exercising in front of a computer is not always easy. In fact, it is almost impossible. Perhaps people should find creative ways to limit Internet use." That is the view of family health specialist Charles Bravo. He would like to see young people spend as much time outside as they spend in front of the computer. "Allow yourself to use the computer for as long as you like," he suggests. "But also make sure you trade 'outside' time for computer time. For every minute spent in front of the computer, you should spend a minute being active outside."

"And if getting outside is not an option, at least get up once in a while to walk around and stretch," Bravo advises. "Media is a huge part of our lives. However, people are not meant to sit around all day when they use it. It's just unhealthy. Get up and move!"

A Balanced Life

As these experts have told us, it's all about balance. Working exercise into your life does not require drastic measures. It should not mean taking away the TV and computer. It's more a matter of finding a balance between media time and exercise time. Even if you need to do both together! ∎

Practice the Skill

Recognizing Viewpoint: Persuasion

1. Read pages 100–101. Write the author's viewpoint about exercise and young people. Then write three reasons he gives to support his viewpoint.

Author's Viewpoint	_____
	_____
Reasons	• _____
	_____
	• _____
	_____
	• _____
	_____

2. How does Pete Tillson's experience support the author's viewpoint?

_____

_____

Check Comprehension

1. What event got Pete Tillson hooked on exercise?

_____

_____

2. Look at the bar graph. What was the top online activity for teenagers in 2005?

_____

The Good News

1. Write the viewpoint of Angela Elliott. Then write three reasons she gives to support her viewpoint.

Angela Elliott's Viewpoint
_____
_____

Reasons		
_____	_____	_____
_____	_____	_____
_____	_____	_____
_____	_____	_____

2. What is Charles Bravo's viewpoint?

_____

_____

3. Whose viewpoint is more persuasive? Why?

_____

_____

Vocabulary

Find "set a cap on" on page 102. Explain what it means.

_____

Writing

Does this article persuade you that young people spend too much time using media? Explain.

Media Madness

Hi guys, welcome back to *Media Madness*, the cutting-edge blog for music, movies, and all things entertainment.

What do you want to talk about today? You know what's been bugging me? Music and movie downloads are so expensive! I don't expect to get them for free (though it would be nice), but don't the music and movie companies realize that most of us are still in school? We don't have a whole lot of money. What do you guys think?

Steve

> Which blogger gives the strongest support for his or her viewpoint?

Musicmaven at 8:00 p.m. on Friday August 8, 2008

You're speaking my language, Steve. It took me six months to save up for an MP3 player! And now that I finally have it, the thing's half empty. I can't afford to download more than a couple of songs a week. At the rate I'm going, I'll be in my thirties before I've filled it up!

Tarathebrave at 8:05 p.m. on Friday August 8, 2008

I am sick and tired of the cost of music downloads too. Those bands are just greedy, and the music companies aren't any better. I think they take advantage of us. But does anyone think we can do anything about it?

◀ Previous   Next ▶

Smokeonthewater at 8:12 p.m. on Friday August 8, 2008

Let me set Musicmaven and Tarathebrave straight. I work for a music company. You have no idea how much it costs to produce a song. There is the cost of the studio, the producer, the sound engineer, musicians, and backup singers. Then there are the artists themselves. None of these people work for the music company, but they all need to be paid. And then all the music company's employees have to be paid too. Do you know how many people work in my office? We have 5 people in marketing, 22 people in sales (including me), 16 people in production, 2 Web site designers, and a bunch of managers. Should I go on? Really, think about it, people. How do you think we get paid? By selling the music we produce, that's how! There wouldn't even be any music to download without us. So think again before you complain about prices.

Rebelgirl at 8:20 p.m. on Friday August 8, 2008

Hey, Smokeonthewater, chill! I happen to know a little about the music business too. You forgot to mention the huge profits that companies like yours make. Even if your company cut the cost of a download in half, it would still stay in business. And—if things are a little tight—they could just cut your salary too!

Number1 at 8:23 p.m. on Friday August 8, 2008

You're all living in the dark ages. Only fools actually pay to download music. A friend of mine found a way to download for free. How cool is that? I can get as many songs as I want, without paying a cent.

Indianacowboy at 8:25 p.m. on Friday August 8, 2008

What's your secret, Number1?

Number1 at 8:28 p.m. on Friday August 8, 2008

Like I'm going to tell you.

Lilygrace at 8:45 p.m. on Friday August 8, 2008

You think you're so smart, Number1? One reason that downloads cost so much (for movies and for music) is because some people don't pay their share. That's you I'm talking about. What you're doing is wrong—not to mention illegal. Those of us who buy our music are actually paying for *your* downloads too. What do you think about that?

Number1 at 8:47 p.m. on Friday August 8, 2008

Get over yourself, Lilygrace! You're just mad I won't tell you how to get free music—or free movies, for that matter.

Movienut at 8:56 p.m. on Friday August 8, 2008

I'm glad someone brought up movies as well as music. I download my favorite movies all the time. That way I can watch them any time I want—in the comfort of my own home, or wherever I choose. I don't mind paying for what I watch, but my plan limits the number of movies I can download each month. The problem is, I keep going over my limit, and then I'm hit with a huge bill! What should I do?

Smartalec at 9:00 p.m. on Friday August 8, 2008

Change your plan!

Superstitious13 at 9:23 p.m. on Friday August 8, 2008

Hey, Movienut! How about getting out of the house and actually going to the movies? Watching a movie at home just isn't the same. The screen, the sound, the smell of buttered popcorn, sharing the experience with others—there's nothing like it.

Homebody at 9:30 p.m. on Friday August 8, 2008

You forgot to mention the people who talk through the whole movie, the people who arrive late and climb over you, the uncomfortable seats, and the sticky patches of soda on the floor. Give me the comfort of my own home anytime.

Latenightanimal at 10:00 p.m. on Friday August 8, 2008

Hi, I'm a musician, and I just got home from a gig. None of you has mentioned the most important point about downloading music from the Internet. It gives musicians like me a great way to reach an audience without using a big record label. There were about 200 people at my gig tonight, but my Web site gets about 5,000 hits a month. I have three songs on my site that people can download for free and another twelve that people can pay for if they like what they hear. Promoting my music on the Internet means I can be as creative as I want without having to sell out.

Indiefan at 10:05 p.m. on Friday August 8, 2008

Right on, Latenightanimal. I download tons of songs from bands I've never heard of. Stores don't stock their CDs and the major music sites don't have their songs to download. But their music rocks!!!

Thanks for your comments, guys. If you've got an idea for tomorrow's discussion, drop me a line at steve@mediamadness.com.

Steve

Practice the Skill

Recognizing Viewpoint: Persuasion

1. Write Smokeonthewater's viewpoint. Then list three reasons he gives to support his viewpoint.

Smokeonthewater's Viewpoint	_____ _____
Reasons	• _____ _____ • _____ _____ • _____ _____

2. Does Rebelgirl agree with Smokeonthewater? What is her viewpoint?

_____

_____

3. Whose viewpoint is most persuasive? Why?

_____

_____

Check Comprehension

1. What does Lilygrace think about people who don't pay for downloads?

_____

_____

2. What problem does Movienut have with downloading movies?

_____

_____

Making a Case

1. Superstitious13 and Homebody had different opinions about going to the movies. Write each person's reasons below.

Superstitious13: Go to the movies!	**Homebody:** Stay at home!
• _____ _____ • _____ _____ • _____ _____	• _____ _____ • _____ _____ • _____ _____

2. Whose reasons do you think are most persuasive? Why?

_____

_____

Please Download

Read the response by Latenightanimal. What are two ways musicians benefit from Internet downloading?

• _____

• _____

Vocabulary

Define these words as they are used in the text.

• profits (page 107) _____

• promoting (page 109) _____

Writing

What is your viewpoint on Internet downloading? Write your own response to this blog.

Text Connections

You have read several texts about modern media. Now choose one of the following topics to explore.

▶▶ With a partner, collect movie reviews from newspapers, magazines, and the Internet. How do the reviews persuade readers to see or not see a movie? What reasons and examples do they use to support their opinions? Share your findings with the class.

▶▶ Write a review of a movie that you have seen. Remember to give your opinion along with reasons and examples that support it.

▶▶ As a class, discuss the viewpoint that kids don't get enough exercise because of media. Opinions should be supported by reasons and examples.

▶▶ Write a letter persuading a friend to exercise with you. Include good reasons and examples.

▶▶ Invite your classmates to keep a log of their media time and exercise time for one week with you. Draw a simple graph to display your findings. What would you suggest based on your findings?

▶▶ Design a blog and start a discussion on a topic that you feel strongly about. Ask classmates to reply. Report your findings to the class.

Continue your explorations by reading these books:

Build Your Own Website by Robert L. Perry
Would you like to create your own Web site? This book will show you how.

Escape Key by Michael Coleman
The Internet Detectives call on friends around the world to find an international thief.

Film and Television by Michael and Jane Pelusey
Did you ever wonder how films and television shows are made? Get an insider's look.